The BIBBY *Story*

Conder Mill
Nr. Lancaster

James Bibby Senr., 1812–1897

Founder of the Company

FOREWORD

During the past few years the number of farmers' parties visiting our mills and farms has been steadily increasing and we now entertain some 9,000 to 10,000 customers and friends each year.

We have felt, therefore, that it might be worth while producing a little souvenir to give to each visitor, in the shape of a booklet describing, with illustrations, some of the things they have seen during their visit and some things that they may have missed seeing.

This booklet is the result of our efforts and we trust that it will be found acceptable to our visitors and of some interest to all those into whose hands it may come.

J. BIBBY & SONS LIMITED

March, 1950.

James Bibby
1853–1928

Joseph Bibby
1851–1940

THE BIBBY STORY

THE Business had its roots in a country flour milling business carried on at Conder Mill, near Lancaster, deriving its name from the river on which it was situated and from which it drew its power.

The Mill came into the possession of the family in 1829, through its purchase by Edward Bibby, a native of the neighbouring valley of Wyresdale, after ten years' occupancy as tenant. It is said that he was a man possessed of considerable craftsmanship, and that he himself fashioned the grindstones for his mill from the local stone of the neighbourhood.

Edward Bibby died in 1854 at the age of 74, leaving a family of twelve children, including three sons. The second son, James, took over the Mill, the eldest having emigrated to America and the youngest to New Zealand.

James Bibby continued to operate the Mill and the farm as his father had done before him, until he was well over 60, and then, possibly with a view to finding an opening for his sons, opened a warehouse in Lancaster for the sale of flour and provender.

A few years later, at the age of 66, he entered into partnership with his two younger sons, Joseph and James, to carry on this undertaking, the name "J. Bibby and Sons" being adopted in 1878.

The two younger partners, then aged 27 and 25 respectively, were the active spirits behind the new undertaking, and were at this time considering the idea of making and introducing a Calf Meal for rearing calves with less raw milk than was then customary.

This idea was in due course translated into practical effect, and met with some success. It was followed by Dairy Meal and Fattening Meal, and later, presses were installed for the manufacture of Compound Cakes.

The senior partner viewed with amazement, and sometimes with misgivings, we are told, the rapid growth of the business. However, nothing appeared to be able to stop it, and seven years or so after its inception it became evident that the Lancaster premises were becoming inadequate. Auxiliary premises were considered, and eventually taken in the shape of the upper floors of two warehouses in Liverpool during 1885. The Head Office was transferred to Liverpool in August 1888.

Incidentally, it might be mentioned that Liverpool was familiar ground to the senior partner who, for many years before the railway from the north opened, had made periodic visits to the city to sell the products of his flour mill and buy provender for his warehouse. In those days he made the journey on horseback, and it is told that he put up on these occasions at a hostelry in Dale Street. It is a tribute to his genial personality that although a staunch teetotaller he was always a very welcome guest at the inn.

The business in Liverpool was soon established with Joseph and James Bibby at the head of affairs, and it grew and prospered.

About 1890 the first crushing presses were installed, and this constituted an important step, as it marked the entry of the Company into the old and important industry of seed-crushing, which offered endless scope to those who sought it.

During the period 1890-1900 rapid strides continued to be made, though checked for a time by a disastrous fire in 1892, which swept away the greater part of the Liverpool premises.

The Original Warehouse
Lancaster

The fire, however, proved to be a blessing in disguise, and cleared the site for more suitable buildings. James Bibby Senior died in 1897 at the age of 85. Through his death the Company lost a founder of whom it might well be proud. He was a man of outstanding character, and his influence upon the business was undoubtedly powerful and lasting.

By the beginning of the new century Bibby's Mills were well established in Liverpool and gradually becoming known throughout the country. At this time the number of employees totalled about 800.

During the following years, and up to the present time, steady and substantial progress has continued to be made, and a few milestones may be mentioned in chronological order:

1910   Opening of new Office Building in King Edward Street. This date roughly coincides with the introduction of women to clerical work in the Office.

1911   Explosion in Compound Cake Factory.

1916   Completion of new Oil Mill.

1919   Introduction of Family Allowances.

1920   Beginning of serious incursion into Soap industry.

1924   Introduction of Compound Cooking Fats.
        Inauguration of Pensions.

1925   Purchase of Experimental Farm at
        Puddington.

1928   Death of James Bibby.

1930   Explosion in Storage Silos.

1931   Introduction of Trex (Cooking Fat).
        Introduction of Oil Expellers (latest method of
        removing oil from oil seeds).

1940   Death of Joseph Bibby, aged 89. He will no
        doubt be well remembered among our older
        farmer friends as the author and publisher of
        the famous "Bibby's Annual", the last issue of
        which was published in 1936.

1942   A Company, under the title of Brown and
        Bibby Ltd., was formed to take over the
        Printing Department (The P.P. Press) which
        produced the "Bibby" Calendar, Bibby's
        "Hearth & Farm" and the greater part of
        our advertising and other literature.

At the present time J. Bibby and Sons Limited
employ approximately 4,000 persons, and the Company is controlled by ten Directors, nine of whom are
members of the family, whose concern it is to ensure

that the tradition of quality and service established by Edward Bibby 120 years ago is maintained in accordance with the times.

THE COMPANY'S PRODUCTS

ANIMAL FEEDING STUFFS

These fall naturally into two categories; firstly, there are the "Straight Cakes" which are the primary products of the oil mill, resulting from the crushing of the raw materials—Groundnuts, Linseed, Cottonseed, Sunflowerseed, etc., by hydraulic or expeller presses so that part of the oil is separated from the seed.

At the present time of course, most of the oilcake mentioned above is ground and blended with grains, cereal products, molasses, minerals, etc., to make the second category of feeding stuffs, namely "Compounds", which foods are suitable for feeding to cattle, pigs and poultry.

It is our aim to be able to supply our farmer friends with "A feed for every need", and to this end we manufacture a great variety of brands in the form of "Cakettes", "Pellets" and "Meal". Our Experimental Farms and Research Laboratory work together, constantly seeking to improve the quality and value of the Bibby brands.

Vegetable Oils

Various types of vegetable oils are obtained by means of crushing, expelling and extracting oilseeds. These oils, after refining when necessary, are used by ourselves and other manufacturers in the production of cooking fats and soap. Crude and refined oils are also sold to manufacturers of margarine and other foodstuffs. Linseed oil is sold for use in the manufacture of paint and linoleum.

Lecithin

This is a valuable extract obtained from certain crude vegetable oils. It is an emulsifying agent, and as such finds extensive use in the chocolate and margarine trades, and being rich in phosphorus it also has a nutritional value. Lecithin is also supplied to the rubber and leather trades.

Soaps

Our principal proprietary brands for domestic use are:

> *Bibby Soap and Bibby Carbolic.* Pure soaps of the finest quality for all household purposes, made from vegetable oils.
>
> *Glee.* A high-grade soap powder equally suitable for washing clothes, dishes, etc.

Araby. A fine, triple milled white toilet soap, delicately perfumed.

Clozone. A special soap in the form of fine filaments, particularly recommended for cleaning all fabrics.

Bibby Soap Flakes. Purest concentrated soap in fine flakes, readily soluble in warm water and specially suitable for washing delicate woollens, silks, etc.

Bibby Dairy Cleanser. An entirely new detergent especially prepared for the thorough cleansing of dairy utensils without injurious effects on milking-machine parts or rubber. Also for washing dishes and household utensils.

In addition to these domestic soaps, we also manufacture many different types for export, as well as special soaps required for laundry and textile use.

GLYCERINE

Glycerine is a by-product in the manufacture of soap. We sell it in the crude state, and after further treatment it is used in the manufacture of explosives, pharmaceutical preparations and for many other purposes.

TREX

A domestic cooking fat made entirely from vegetable oils which has established an excellent reputation amongst housewives for its convenience and digestibility. (We hope to resume manufacture as soon as the Government decontrols margarine and cooking fats).

COMPOUND COOKING FATS

These are supplied to the bakery and confectionery trades and to fish friers.

RESEARCH AND DEVELOPMENT

It is the Company's policy to pay special attention to research. On the mechanical side, new crushing, extracting and other machinery has been developed, thus ensuring that the processes are as efficient and up-to-date as possible. On the chemical side, research is constantly proceeding in our laboratories to find new outlets for our products and to develop entirely new lines. The processes used in the works are kept under review, and adjustments are frequently made with the object of improving the quality of our products and reducing the cost of manufacture.

Head Office
Liverpool

Many of our friends visit us each year in Liverpool, and in the following pages we have endeavoured so far as is possible to remind you of your tour of our Mills and Farms, and to fill in some of the gaps that are inevitable when there is so much to see in such a short time.

Oil Seeds being discharged into barges. This is done to facilitate the handling of bulk cargoes where there is difficulty in getting large cargo vessels alongside our warehouses.

One of our warehouses showing elevators unloading oilseeds and grain from barges.

The top floor of one of the warehouses, showing the shutes through which the raw materials are received from the barges.

Deodorising plant, showing the control panels. It is here, under vacuum and at a high temperature, that the oils are refined.

Soap Boiling Pans. Various oils and fats together with caustic soda being boiled by steam from open pipes.

Soap Coolers. The picture shows slabs of newly made soap being taken from the cooler. Each slab weighs approximately 100 *lbs.*

The Flake Machine. Soap enters at one end in liquid form and is cooled, rolled, cut and dried, the finished soap flakes emerging from the other end in a steady stream.

"Araby" Toilet Soap is made in this room. This group of machines handles the soap flakes, produced in the machine shown above, to which are added perfumes. The finished tablets emerge neatly wrapped ready for despatch.

*Box Making
Department.*

*We use thousands
of wooden boxes
annually to carry
our export Soap
and Cooking Fats
to many different
countries.*

*Under hygienic conditions our Cooking Fats are packed, weighed and despatched for
consumption both at home and abroad.*

"Glee" Soap Powder is made in this entirely enclosed machine on the tenth floor of the Soap Works.

These Soap Boiling Pans each contain 100 tons of soap and are suspended above the seventh floor in the new Soapery. When the boiling is completed, the liquid soap is drawn through the pipes shown underneath the pans.

The "Clozone" Machine. "Clozone" consists of fine filaments of pure soap—ideal for washing delicate fabrics.

Soap Powder Packing Machines. Each machine packs, weighs, seals and delivers 7,200 cartons per hour.

(Left)

A view of the Oil Mill Building.

(Below)

The invention of the Hydraulic Press paved the way to the great expansion of the Seed Crushing Industry during the latter half of the last century. It is now being superseded by the Expeller.

(Left)

The Expeller is a mechanical screw press. It possesses all the advantages of mechanisation. By its use, much of the arduous labour associated with Seed Crushing is eliminated.

(Below)

The Delinter is used to remove the cotton fibres which clothe cotton seed on arrival in this country. This process greatly improves the resultant cake.

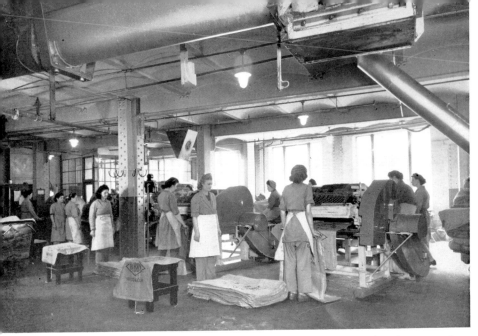

The Sack Printers at work. These machines are capable of printing about 5,000 bags per hour.

Mixing Tables for Compound Foods. These ensure constant, steady and thorough mixing of any brand as desired.

Two of the Pellet dressing machines over which all the Poultry Pellets pass to ensure that they are of correct size and free from meal or lumps before being packed.

In the Poultry Food Section. A view of some of the Pellet-making machines showing the automatic signal which warns the operators when the machine needs attention.

One of the "Cakelette" Units. The meal is prepared in the kettle shown in the background and, when cooked and mixed with molasses, is fed into these rolls which press the meal gently but firmly together, forming "Cakelettes".

Part of the "Cakelette" plant, showing gravity bucket elevators conveying meal for processing.

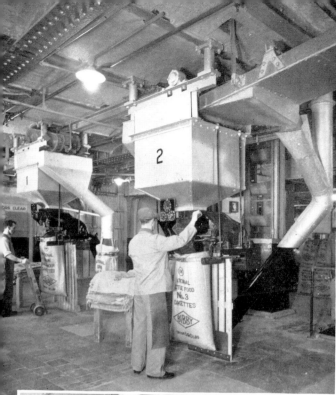

*Bagging "Cakettes".
After the cake is cooled
it comes to these hoppers,
where it is weighed and
packed.*

A loading bay showing lorries being loaded from a conveyor.

A view of the Despatch Department. This floor is immediately above our Railway Siding, and bags are seen being lowered into the wagons below. At the far end, lorries are loaded for road delivery.

Our Siding. Hundreds of railway wagons leave the Mills every week conveying Bibby Feeding Stuffs to our local depots throughout the Country.

"A Feed for Every Need." Some of our brands ready for inspection by our visitors.

A section of the Laboratory, where tests are carried out hourly to ensure the purity of our various products.

A view of the Mills from Great Howard Street, Liverpool.

Our Mills occupy several blocks, and communication over the intervening streets is maintained by bridges, some of which you see here crossing Formby Street (nine wagons can be loaded at once in this street).

In the shadow of the Oil Mill. The horse has not yet lost its place in dockland, and the Liverpool carter is particularly proud of his Shires, some of which are seen here.

Neptune Street—raw materials arriving at the Mills.

YOU have now seen how we receive the raw material into our warehouses and have followed, stage by stage, the various processes that provide feeding stuffs for the farmer, soap for the housewife and for export, and cooking fats for the frying pans of the nation . . .

And so we move over (or under) the Mersey to the Experimental Farms in the Wirral Peninsula.

VIEW OF THE "BIBBY" MILLS FROM THE AIR

Situated by the side of the River Mersey and convenient to rail and road services, our Mills have been designed for the speedy and economical processing of raw materials.

Warehouse. Oil Mill. Old Soapery. New Soapery.

J.Coburn. Witherop. 1949.

Oil Refinery.   Mill Office.   Head Office.

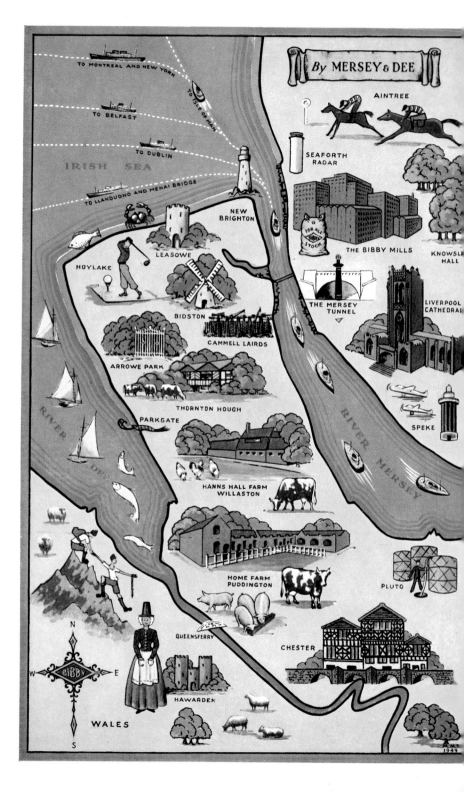

By MERSEY & DEE

THE FARMS

WE run two experimental farms in Cheshire, one at Puddington and one at Hanns Hall, Willaston. At Puddington there is a first-class dairy herd, and work is done on the nutrition of cattle and fattening of pigs, and on general agricultural problems. At Willaston, experiments are carried out in the nutrition, health and rearing of poultry and pigs. Both farms are open to inspection by our customers, and a technical advisory service is run in connection with them.

Very occasionally we are called upon to test foodstuffs which are suspected of having caused trouble to our customers' stock. In such cases a thorough investigation is carried out on these farms, in conjunction with our Veterinary Department with a view to finding the cause of the trouble. Incidentally, we may say that the goods are usually eaten readily by our "control" animals without any ill effects, thus suggesting that food is often blamed for ills for which it is not responsible.

HOME FARM, PUDDINGTON

Comprises about 410 acres, consisting of 340 acres purchased in 1925 together with a nearby smallholding of 28½ acres added in 1946 and 42 acres rented.

Soil

It is good cropping soil, medium to heavy loam, and provides useful pasture for the cows from late April to November. Visitors often remark on the quality of grass at Puddington after a period of drought, compared with other parts of the country.

Buildings

The buildings are well constructed in a warm red brick which forms a nice contrast to the rectangular grass plot around which they are built. The present layout consists of cowhouse with 104 standings, stabling for six horses, individual calf pens, calving boxes, loose boxes, a bullock house, two bull pens, a cheese-making dairy and a piggery built above the loose boxes. Although we are restricted in the purchase of feeding stuffs in the same manner as all other farmers, it is hoped, in the very near future, to bring back into use the large Scandinavian-type fattening house for pigs, in which we shall conduct experiments in connection with feeding problems.

Dairy Herd

Foot and mouth disease broke out in 1941 and the whole herd of Shorthorns had to be slaughtered, but two months later was replaced with a commercial herd of Attested Ayrshires, including some pedigree beasts. None of the original herd is now left and the present herd is composed of approximately 100 cows, 120 head of young stock and two pedigree bulls, all of which are home bred with the exception of the younger bull, "Burton Daring" (Vol. 67); both bulls are grandsons of "Bargower Golden Future".

Pigs

These are bought in as stores from Hanns Hall to be fattened, using the whey which is a valuable by-product from the cheese-making. It is drained into a tank sunk in the ground in front of the dairy, and pumped up to the piggeries built over the loose boxes, bull pens, etc. This lay-out is very satisfactory, being economical in labour and space, but allowing the pigs to get plenty of fresh air and sunshine. The unique arrangement for the disposal of manure is another labour-saving feature. Before food rationing was introduced approximately 1,000 pigs were fattened each year on the farm, the Scandinavian piggery being also in use.

Research

Research into feeding problems is continually being carried out at Puddington with experiments on pigs, calves and dairy cows.

During the period of food shortages and at the request of the Ministries of Food and Agriculture, our normal research work has been augmented from time to time by experiments conducted with a view to helping the food supply. It may be interesting to record three such experiments.

(1) *Urea Substitute for Protein*

This experiment was carried out to find a protein substitute but the results showed that it was not a practical proposition to use urea in cattle foods.

(2) *Iodinated Protein*

This was fed to a group of cows in order to see whether the milk yield could be maintained in mid-lactation when normally it gradually falls. Iodine is known to stimulate the thyroid, which in turn affects the vital processes of the body, e.g., accelerating the heart-beat and the burning up of body fats, increasing milk production, etc. The milk yield was kept up and therefore the total was considerably increased, but it was found that, unless the iodinated protein was carefully used under Veterinary supervision, serious ill-effects on the health of the animals would result, so its general use has never been sanctioned.

(3) Rubber Seed Meal

This has been tried as an added source of protein for dairy cattle. Recent experiments have given very good results. Further tests will be made when more supplies are available.

Low Solids-not-Fats

It has been observed during the past few years that the solids-not-fats in milk are lower during the winter months than while the cows are out at grass. This was not our usual experience in pre-war days—rather the contrary.

There is a good deal of evidence now to show that war-time rations supply the explanation, and the non-fatty solids in milk tend to decline when the cows' ration is inadequate in protein and in starch equivalent value.

We are, at present, conducting a test to demonstrate the extent to which poor feeding can reduce the non-fatty solids in milk.

Herd Policy

The attested herd of cows is being line-bred for

performance to bring up the herd average milk yield while maintaining a high level of fertility and stamina.

We have recently begun to dehorn the calves at an early age, with a view ultimately to having a herd, the members of which are deprived of the means of harrying and injuring one another.

While the calves are on the bucket, they are reared in small single pens and afterwards in open yards until they are old enough to be turned out.

Vaccination of all calves before six months of age is practised to keep the herd free from contagious abortion.

Cheese-making

In normal times cheese-making is carried out throughout the year, as this is found to be more profitable than the sale of liquid milk, and the main income is derived from this source; in addition to which, from cheese-making, we also obtain a substantial quantity of whey for our pigs.

Farmhouse cheese-making, originally the main outlet for milk produced in Cheshire, is rapidly dying out and it is interesting to note that there are to-day less than forty farms engaged in this industry in the county. Our output is on the average four to five cheeses daily, each weighing from 30 to 60 pounds.

Aerial views of Home Farm, Puddington.

"Welcome, ladies and gentlemen, to Home Farm Puddington." A party of visitors is greeted by the Farm Manager.

Some of the Dairy Herd out at grass.

Another more general view of the herd grazing at Puddington.

Milking Time.

Some baconers in the "Upstairs" Piggery at Puddington.

The Ayrshire herd coming in for milking.

The Bull pens and a general view of the "Upstairs" Piggery and loose boxes at Puddington.

One of the Shippons.

HANNS HALL FARM, WILLASTON

This farm was taken over in April 1936, mainly as a Poultry Farm, but it is now run on intensive lines as a mixed farm.

Acreage. 270 acres, of which 110 acres are arable, the rest leys. The poultry use about 60 acres.

Soil. The soil is light, with sandstone subsoil that dries out rapidly, so it is well suited to poultry.

Buildings. The original out-of-date premises were demolished and the present light airy buildings were erected round three sides of a large central lawn. They consist of a farrowing house with 16 pens, shippon with standings for 38 cows, the dairy, stables, loose boxes, workshop and a garage. The two bulls are housed across the yard under a separate roof.

In the poultry section of the farm are the main offices, canteen, egg rooms, incubator room and plucking room. These buildings will have to be enlarged in the near future to meet the growing demands made upon them.

Poultry. The standing poultry population is about 1,600 laying hens, and under the Ministry of Agriculture and Fisheries' Poultry Stock Improvement

Plan the farm is accredited in both Breeders' and Commercial Stock Suppliers' Grades.

During the summer the total number goes as high as 7,000 birds, the main breeds being Light Sussex, Rhode Island Reds and Brown Leghorns, with some cross-breds from these three types, and about 150 stock cockerels. Four cabinet electric incubators are in use during the hatching season, with a capacity of 9,000, 6,000, 3,000 and 2,000 eggs respectively, but the increasing demand for day-old chicks far exceeds the supply.

REARING SYSTEMS

Brooder houses of various types, movable or fixed and heated by electricity, oil or hot water, are used.

Pullets are trap-nested in eight laying houses each with a capacity of 100 birds, divided into two sections of 50 birds and surrounded by its own alternate grazing pens.

There are a number of breeding pens used for individual breeding and progeny tests.

There are 80 fold units in use. These have been found to be suitable for all ages, from day-old chicks to laying hens. This method of rearing has a very beneficial effect on the pasture as long as the folds are moved regularly.

A laying battery for 500 birds has provided very useful data about the health and performance of poultry kept intensively, and their feeding and labour requirements under this system. This is being augmented by a second battery to house 1,000 birds.

Dairy Stock. Although many of the foundation cows were non-pedigree, grading up to good bulls is in progress, and eventually only pedigree animals will be retained.

The herd of Attested Ayrshires consists of 36 dairy cows, young stock and two bulls, totalling approximately 100 animals.

Pigs. Only 15 to 20 pedigree Large White sows and a boar are kept at the present time owing to feeding restrictions, but breeding results have been very satisfactory, as will be seen from the following table.

	No. of litters	Average No. of pigs born per litter	Average No. of pigs weaned per litter	Average weight at weaning (8 weeks)
1944/45 ...	18	13·1	9·0	28·4 lbs.
1945/46 ...	26	13·3	9·7	29·8 ,,
1946/47 ...	17	12·3	8·5	33·4 ,,
1947/48 ...	18	14·5	9·6	31·0 ,,
1948/49 ...	21	12·6	8·8	30·8 ,,

Young pigs are sold for breeding purposes, or to Home Farm, Puddington, for fattening.

Sheep. Some 45 Clun ewes and about 75 lambs are maintained to keep the poultry runs closely grazed.

Experimental Work (in progress at time of going to press).

Poultry

(1) The relationship of the Vitamin B complex and in particular the importance of the Animal Protein Factor in the nutrition of young and adult stock.

(2) Feeding different grains, barley, maize, oats, wheat.

(3) Rearing birds under the American intensive system for table poultry.

Pigs

(1) Feeding Cubes versus Meal.

(2) Feeding Vitamin B Supplement.

Policy. Great importance is attached to the management of the pastures with regular applications of lime and phosphates so that animals obtain their minerals in the herbage; catch crops and silage receive special attention, and have given very good results on this farm.

The majority of the young stock are left out all the year round except in very severe weather.

The policy in regard to poultry-breeding is centred on progeny testing, selection being based on families, not individuals. Different systems of rearing and housing are practised for trial and demonstration.

Sales of young pigs, fat lambs, bull calves, stock cockerels and day-old chicks show a good turnover; the tuberculosis-free milk, bottled on the farm, is in great demand locally.

During the past few years a short Annual Course has been held in conjunction with the National Federation of Young Farmers' Clubs, dealing with either poultry or dairy farming. These courses appear to have been a great success.

On both farms short courses in Agricultural subjects, both theoretical and practical, are given to certain of our employees.

Permission has also been given for the farms to be used by the University of Liverpool Veterinary Field Station, established at "Leahurst" nearby, for teaching purposes to enable students to obtain practical experience under field conditions, and to make available any data which would further research into problems of animal health.

An aerial view of Hanns Hall Farm, Willaston, showing the lay-out of the experimental poultry runs.

Aerial view of the buildings, barns and dairy at Hanns Hall Farm.

Poultry Breeding Pens at Hanns Hall. (Some of the sheep used for keeping the grass short may be seen in this picture).

These birds are undergoing progeny testing. Over a period of twelve months accurate records are kept of Production, Fertility, Hatchability and Mortality.

Light Sussex Pullets in their pen. These birds are undergoing egg-laying and feeding trials, and are ringed and trap-nested so that accurate records may be kept.

A view showing the lay-out of the runs.

Milking Time at Hanns Hall.

Some Large White sows and their litters happily foraging in the paddock.

In-pig Large White sow.

"*After the event.*" *A sturdy litter of eight.*

Light Sussex Cockerel and Hens.

These birds have already undergone the Progeny Test and are now being used as foundation stock.

A close-up of a trial pen of pullets on test.

Summer scene at Willaston.

Hanns Hall Dairy Herd of Ayrshires.

At the end of their day's visit we snap a party of farmers while one of the younger members proudly walks our young bull.

CONCLUSION

*"Whoever could make two ears of corn, or
two blades of grass, to grow upon a spot of
ground where only one grew before, would
deserve better of mankind, and do more essential
service to his country, than the whole race of
Politicians put together."*

SWIFT.

If this be the aim of the Agriculturist,
that of the Industrialist must surely be to
produce a better quality article, quicker
and more cheaply than before.

This has been the aim of our Company
since it was founded and we believe that the
growth of our business has indicated some
measure of success in this direction.

We hope that your visit to us, of which
this book is a souvenir, has served to show
that our efforts are still continuing and has
brought to you a closer understanding of
our activities.

*Photographs by Stewart Bale Ltd
and A. Baumann*

*You will doubtless recognize
many familiar faces among the
group in the photograph opposite,
which was taken upon the occas-
ion of your recent visit to our
Mills and Farms.*